SULPHURIC ACID

"It is no exaggeration to say that we may fairly judge of the commercial prosperity of a country from the amount of sulphuric acid it consumes."

FAMILIAR LETTERS ON CHEMISTRY
Justus von Liebig. 1843. p.31

SULPHURIC

ACID

MANUFACTURE AND USES

Made and printed in Great Britain
at The Kynoch Press · Witton · Birmingham, 6
For the publishers, Imperial Chemical Industries Limited

LONDON, S.W.1

1955

FOREWORD

IT is often difficult for the student to relate the chemistry learned at school to that same chemistry as it is applied in industrial practice. Reactions carried out in glass apparatus on the bench are lost inside great steel towers and reaction chambers in the chemical factory. Manufacturing processes change as more efficient techniques are discovered or to meet the fluctuating demands of industry.

This book has been prepared by Imperial Chemical Industries Ltd., with the assistance of the Science Masters' Association, to provide a link between the classroom and industry in the case of one important heavy chemical—sulphuric acid. It describes the manufacture and uses of sulphuric acid under modern industrial conditions.

PRICE FIVE SHILLINGS

CONTENTS

INTRODUCTION

Sulphuric acid is probably the most widely used of all manufactured chemicals. There are few consumer goods that do not need sulphuric acid at some stage or other in their production.

As Justus von Liebig said more than a hundred years ago, consumption of this acid is a reliable guide to a country's industrial vitality.

In Britain, sulphuric acid manufacture has been carried on since the early eighteenth century. It is an integral part of the chemical industry of the country, and the acid has become a raw material essential to the nation's prosperity.

A
MANUFACTURE

There are two established methods of manufacturing sulphuric acid, (a) the *Chamber Process* and (b) the *Contact Process*.

In each the basic chemical principles are the oxidation of sulphur dioxide to sulphur trioxide, followed by combination of the sulphur trioxide with water to form sulphuric acid:

$$S + O_2 \rightarrow SO_2$$
$$2SO_2 + O_2 \rightarrow 2SO_3$$
$$SO_3 + H_2O \rightarrow H_2SO_4$$

The sulphur dioxide needed in both processes is produced mainly by burning sulphur or sulphur-containing materials in air. Some of the sulphur dioxide used for making sulphuric acid in Britain is obtained from anhydrite (calcium sulphate). In other countries, gypsum (hydrated calcium sulphate) is used also.

RAW MATERIALS

1. Sulphur

(a) Occurrence

Sulphur occurs native in many parts of the world.

Iceland, Teneriffe and St. Vincent used to supply sulphur in the early days of sulphuric acid manufacture. Deposits of sulphur have been found in Sicily, Unalaska and Akun Islands in the Aleutians, in China, Japan and Formosa, New Zealand and other countries (see table below).

Until the beginning of the present century, Sicily supplied the world with most of its sulphur and held a virtual monopoly of sulphur production. Since then, the successful exploitation of underground sulphur beds in Louisiana and Texas in the U.S.A. has changed the situation to such an extent that America now produces more than 90% of the world's sulphur.

The American sulphur deposits were discovered in 1868 by oil prospectors. After the Civil War a well was sunk at Calcascieu in Louisiana. It produced little oil, but the drilling carried evidence of beds of pure sulphur. Experts surveyed the deposit and predicted that, if it could be mined, it contained enough sulphur to make the country independent of Sicilian supplies.

Stimulated by the discovery, mining companies made many attempts to sink conventional shafts into the sulphur deposits. But the sulphur was covered by quicksands; normal mining techniques proved useless and the companies eventually gave up.

This sulphur deposit, and others which have since been discovered in Louisiana and Texas, are domes of porous sulphur-bearing limestone thrust up through the earth's crust as though by a giant finger of rock. Above the domes there is normally a layer of limestone, and on top of this are quicksand and gravel. Below the sulphur there is a layer of anhydrite, below which is often a vast column of rock salt.

The sulphur beds average 125 ft. in thickness. They lie about 500 ft. below the surface of the earth; some are three miles or more in diameter.

At the time of their discovery the sulphur domes were estimated to contain more than 40 million tons of sulphur. They were therefore an industrial prize of tremendous value to America if a way of extracting the sulphur could be found.

In 1890 the problem was solved by Herman Frasch, research director of an American oil company. Frasch patented a process for pumping molten sulphur out of the domes. In December 1894 Frasch started producing his first sulphur, and his process has worked successfully to the present day. It has enabled America to become the world's main source of elemental sulphur.

In 1951 5,363,000 metric tons of sulphur were produced in America, almost entirely by the Frasch process. Production in other countries was as follows:

	metric tons
Italy (including Sicily) ..	223,000
Japan	142,000
Chile	30,100
France	27,500
Algeria	16,100
Spain	9,000
Bolivia	7,800
Argentine	7,700
Turkey	7,400
Peru	2,300

9

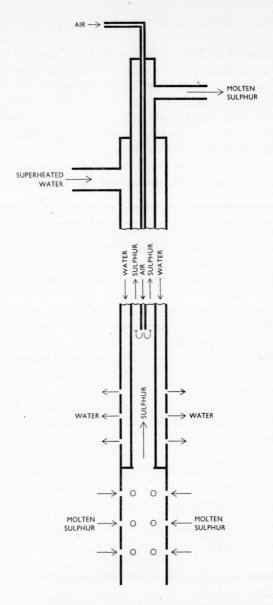

Diagram of Frasch well used in sulphur extraction

(b) Extraction

SICILIAN EXTRACTION PROCESS. The traditional method of extracting sulphur from surface ores has been practised in Sicily for hundreds of years. It consists in burning a portion of the rock sulphur to provide enough heat to melt the remainder and allow it to flow away from the impurities.

The process is crude and uneconomic, involving a loss of as much as 40% of the total sulphur.

A more modern method, used particularly in the extraction of richer ores containing over 25% of sulphur, is to heat the ore in perforated kettles so that the sulphur drains away through holes in the base.

FRASCH PROCESS. The Frasch method of extracting sulphur from underground deposits has remained basically unchanged since the original patent was taken out in 1890. It involves the injection of superheated water into the sulphur and afterwards raising the molten sulphur to the surface with the help of compressed air.

A stout casing is first sunk into the top of the sulphur deposit. Into this is lowered a 6 in. diameter pipe, inside which, in turn, goes a 3 in. diameter pipe which rests on a collar inside the 6 in. pipe within a few feet of the bottom. (The dimensions of these concentric pipes vary in modern wells, but the operating principles remain identical.)

Water is superheated to a temperature of 170–180° C. and forced under pressure down the 6 in. tube. The water enters the porous sulphur-bearing rock through perforations above the collar. Molten sulphur (m.p. 115° C.) flows down, forming a pool at the bottom of the pipe, then rises up the inner tube to within about 300 ft. of the surface. Compressed air is pumped down a 1 in. diameter tube lying inside the 3 in. pipe. The air bubbles through the molten sulphur and water, lowering the specific gravity of the mixture and forming an emulsion which rises to the top of the well. Here it flows out into vats, where the sulphur solidifies.

Modern sulphur wells bring up 6,000 tons of sulphur a day and will pump for three or four months before a new shaft has to be sunk.

Boling Dome in Texas has been producing more than a million tons of sulphur a year since 1929. It has been estimated that, at this production rate, it will not be exhausted until 1970.

Sulphur produced by the Frasch process is normally over 99·8% pure.

2. Iron Pyrites

Iron pyrites, a sulphide of iron (FeS_2), is mined in many countries. Spain, Norway and Cyprus are important exporters.

With a theoretical sulphur content of about 53%, pyrites is a valuable source of sulphur for sulphuric acid manufacture.

The ore used in practice generally contains about 45% of sulphur.

Pyrites normally contains small quantities of other metals, some of which are valuable. Copper, silver and gold are sometimes recovered from the ores after roasting. Rio Tinto pyrites (from Spain), which is used in the U.K., contains 47–48% of sulphur, 40% of iron, less than 0·5% of copper, and a trace of silver.

3. Spent Oxide

In the purification of coal-gas, producer gas and water gas, large quantities of iron oxide are used for removing hydrogen sulphide.

The gas is normally passed through layers of hydrated ferric oxide until a high proportion of ferrous sulphide and sulphur has been formed. Exposure of the mixture to air then reconverts the sulphide to oxide, and liberates more sulphur. These alternate processes of absorption and regeneration continue until the mixture contains more than 50% of free sulphur.

This "spent oxide" is roasted to provide sulphur dioxide for sulphuric acid manufacture. After burning, the oxide can be mixed with various forms of organic matter and used again for removing hydrogen sulphide from gases.

4. Zinc Blende

Zinc blende, or zinc sulphide (ZnS), one of the main sources of zinc, is also a source of sulphur. It is mined in large quantities in Canada, Australia, U.S.A., Mexico and Germany.

The first stage in metal production is to roast the ore to zinc oxide; the sulphur is converted into sulphur dioxide for sulphuric acid manufacture:
$$2ZnS + 3O_2 \rightarrow 2ZnO + 2SO_2$$

5. Anhydrite

Anhydrite, or calcium sulphate ($CaSO_4$), is mined in Britain at Billingham (Co. Durham) and near Carlisle. Some of the sulphuric acid manufactured in Britain is made from sulphur dioxide produced from this mineral. At Billingham the anhydrite mine is situated beneath the factory of the Billingham Division of I.C.I. About a million tons of anhydrite are brought from a depth of 800 ft. every year and used for making ammonium sulphate and sulphuric acid. A plant using this anhydrite as the source of sulphur for sulphuric acid has been operating at Billingham since 1930. It produces approximately 100,000 tons of acid a year (1951). A similar amount of cement is obtained from the calcium oxide residues.

SULPHUR DIOXIDE PRODUCTION

Production of sulphur dioxide from sulphur-containing raw materials is carried out in a number of different ways.

1. Sulphur Burning

There are many kinds of sulphur burners. The three main types are (1) rotary tubes, (2) towers packed with chequer brickwork and fed with molten sulphur pumped in at the top with co-current air, and (3) furnaces fed with molten sulphur pumped through a "gun" type burner similar to those used for burning oil.

In all cases a stream of air provides oxygen for the combustion, and the sulphur dioxide produced is ready for use with a minimum of purification:

$$S + O_2 \rightarrow SO_2$$

2. Pyrites Burning

Pyrites is burnt in furnaces similar to those described later for spent oxide or in a rotary kiln about 100 ft. in length. The kiln slopes slightly, so that the pyrites fed in at the higher end travels slowly through the kiln to the lower end. The sulphur in the pyrites burns to sulphur dioxide, and iron oxide is discharged from the lower end of the kiln:

$$4FeS_2 + 11O_2 \rightarrow 2Fe_2O_3 + 8SO_2$$

The kiln is constructed of steel lined with refractory bricks.

Gas leaving the rotary kiln contains about 7% of SO_2, 10·5% of oxygen and 82·5% of nitrogen. Impurities from the pyrites normally include arsenious oxide and chlorides.

If the gas is to be used in the Contact Process it must be purified. This is carried out in five stages:

1. Gravity-settling of heavy dust.
2. Electrostatic precipitation of finer dust particles. The gas passes electrodes having a potential of 50,000 volts, with the result that the

13

dust particles are given strong electric charges. They are then attracted to oppositely charged plates, where the charges become neutralised. The discharged particles fall into collecting hoppers below.

3. The gas passes through cooling and washing towers. As the gas is cooled, condensable impurities come out of the gas phase.
4. On further cooling, the humidified gas yields droplets of moisture which form round the finest dust nuclei and are readily removed in wet electrostatic precipitators.
5. The gas is thoroughly dried by passing up a drying tower as a counter-current to a stream of concentrated sulphuric acid.

The gas, now clean and dry, is ready to be used for the production of sulphuric acid.

3. Spent Oxide Burning

Spent oxide is fed into the top of a furnace which is divided horizontally by shelves. These shelves act as hearths on which the spent oxide burns. A revolving central shaft drives rakes round on each shelf. The teeth of the rakes are set so that the spent oxide on the top shelf is worked towards the centre, where it falls on to the second shelf from which it is worked outwards to fall on to the shelf below, and so on.

When the charge reaches the bottom of the furnace the sulphur has burned, leaving a relatively sulphur-free residue consisting largely of iron oxide.

Air for the combustion enters at ports in the sides of the furnace.

The iron oxide residue may be returned to the gasworks and after reconstituting is re-used for the recovery of sulphur until the spent oxide is again ready for burning.

Gas leaving the burner contains about 7% of sulphur dioxide with about 8% of oxygen and $3\frac{1}{2}$% of carbon dioxide. The balance is mainly nitrogen, with some water vapour from the combustion of organic matter in the spent oxide.

After going through a settling chamber to remove dust, the gas is ready for use in the Chamber Process.

4. From Anhydrite

Anhydrite is a stable material and cannot readily be broken down into its constituents. Heat alone does not decompose it to any extent until the temperature exceeds 1200° C., and even at 1400° C., which is above the melting point of natural anhydrite, the decomposition pressure is only about 50 mm.:

$$2CaSO_4 \rightarrow 2CaO + 2SO_2 + O_2$$

The thermal decomposition of anhydrite is assisted by the addition of acidic oxides such as silica, ferric oxide and alumina, which combine with the calcium oxide formed, but these mixtures also have only a relatively low decomposition pressure at workable temperatures. Sulphur dioxide could be removed from the reaction zone by a stream of gas, but the SO_2 concentration in the gaseous product would be far too low for sulphuric acid manufacture.

Anhydrite can be decomposed by heating with carbon to produce calcium sulphide:

$$CaSO_4 + 2C \rightarrow CaS + 2CO_2$$

The reaction begins at a much lower temperature and is complete below 1000° C., but the calcium sulphide produced still contains all the sulphur present in the original anhydrite. Calcium sulphide will, however, react with more anhydrite to produce sulphur dioxide and lime according to the equation

$$CaS + 3CaSO_4 \rightleftharpoons 4CaO + 4SO_2$$

and the total pressure above the mixture reaches 1 atmosphere at about 1200° C. The reaction is reversible, and the production of sulphur dioxide is assisted by the addition of acidic oxides to remove the lime:

$$SiO_2 + CaO \rightarrow CaSiO_3$$
$$Al_2O_3 + CaO \rightarrow Ca(AlO_2)_2$$

Silica, lime, and iron and aluminium oxides are the main constituents of Portland cement. The action of heat on a mixture of anhydrite and carbon with substances containing silica, ferric and aluminium oxides in the correct proportions will therefore produce a by-product cement clinker besides the sulphur dioxide which is wanted for sulphuric acid manufacture. The main reactions occurring are the reduction of calcium sulphate to calcium sulphide, the interaction of calcium sulphide and calcium sulphate assisted by the acidic oxides, and some decomposition of calcium sulphate direct with silica. The temperature of the solid product is raised to about 1400° C. to convert it into cement clinker, and the reactions are carried out in a rotary kiln, which is the most convenient equipment for the production of clinker.

Anhydrite is ground up with the correct proportion of ashes containing alumina, sand (silica) and coke.

This raw mixture is fed into the rotary kilns, which are huge cylinders 11 ft. in diameter and nearly 100 yards long. They are fired at the opposite end with pulverised coal, and the hot gases pass through the kilns countercurrently to the solid charge.

Sulphur dioxide passes out of the kiln with nitrogen, carbon dioxide, and a small amount of oxygen. The exit gas contains about 9% of sulphur dioxide.

The gas is purified by methods similar to those used for sulphur dioxide produced from pyrites. Dust is removed in cyclones (cyclonic dust separators). Dust-laden gases enter tangentially into the cylindrical upper portion of the cyclone. The outlet is a pipe placed centrally at the top. The gases are forced through at very high speed. The dust particles are thrown to the sides and fall out of the gas stream to the bottom of the cyclone, which is conical in shape.

The gas is cooled and washed. Sulphur dioxide, which dissolves in the water of the wash tower, is removed by passing the solution countercurrent to a stream of air. This sulphur dioxide/air mixture joins the main gas stream, and after the mist and moisture particles have been precipitated electrostatically the gas is dried by scrubbing with sulphuric acid.

The gas, now containing about 6·5% of sulphur dioxide, is passed through blowers which control the flow of gases through the system. The sulphur dioxide is converted to sulphuric acid by the Contact Process.

Production of one ton of sulphuric acid requires 1·66 tons of anhydrite, 0·36 ton of coal and coke and 0·13 ton of sand, and also yields one ton of cement clinker.

ACID PRODUCTION

(a) Chamber Process

The manufacture of sulphuric acid by the Chamber Process began in Britain during the early part of the eighteenth century, at a factory in Twickenham. In 1740 the factory was removed to Richmond following complaints about the fumes.

The process operated was one patented by Joshua Ward, in which sulphur and saltpetre (potassium nitrate) were burned together inside glass globes, each containing a gallon of water and heated in sand. On a commercial scale the glass vessels had a capacity of about 66 gallons. The success of this process resulted in a drop in the price of sulphuric acid from

2s. 6d. an ounce to 2s. 6d. a pound. Saltpetre was quickly replaced by the cheaper sodium nitrate (nitre).

In 1746 the huge glass vessels were replaced by chambers built from sheet lead. Among the first lead chamber plants were those at Prestonpans, which supplied sulphuric acid for the growing textile industry. Batches of sulphur and nitre were run into the lead chambers on iron trolleys.

Initially the lead chambers were cube-shaped boxes measuring up to 10 ft. in each direction. As sulphuric acid manufacture developed, the size of the chambers increased. One of Muspratt's lead chambers used in 1860 measured 140 ft. $\times$ 24$\frac{1}{2}$ ft. $\times$ 20 ft.

During the nineteenth century the Chamber Process became established throughout the world. Modifications were introduced, but the basic process remained essentially unchanged. Sulphur was burned to provide sulphur dioxide; in the presence of nitrogen oxides this then combined with more oxygen and with water to form sulphuric acid.

The mixture of sulphur and nitre (source of nitrogen oxides) was burned in iron pans situated a little above the level of the water inside the lead chamber. After burning had continued for about two hours, steam and air were admitted and the acid vapours allowed to settle. The chamber was then ventilated for three-quarters of an hour and was ready to receive a further charge of sulphur and nitre.

The use of steam had been introduced in 1774, and in 1793 Clément and Désormes improved production by supplying a current of air to the chambers. They showed that the nitrogen oxides acted as conveyors of oxygen to the sulphur dioxide.

By about 1810 the intermittent method of manufacture had been replaced by one in which the sulphur dioxide was introduced continuously into the chambers.

In 1827 Gay-Lussac invented the tower which bears his name today in acid manufacture. He suggested that the nitrogen oxides emerging from the lead chamber could be absorbed by passing them through a tower down which trickled strong sulphuric acid. The original aim of the Gay-Lussac tower was to cut down the nuisance caused by nitrogen oxides escaping into the atmosphere. It did not come into general use until John Glover discovered a method of recovering and re-using the nitrogen oxides from the acid used in it.

In 1859 the first Glover tower in England was erected near Durham. Not only did it effect a great saving in nitre; it contributed in other ways

17

to increasing the efficiency of the process and became generally adopted throughout the industry.

By 1880 the Chamber Process had become established on the basis of the Glover tower, the lead chambers and the Gay-Lussac tower. It has remained so to the present day, later developments being concerned with the design of plant. Ammonia-oxidation units were introduced in place of nitre as a source of oxides of nitrogen.

The Glover Tower

The hot gases from the burners enter the plant at the base of the Glover tower. As they pass upwards through the tower the gases meet a stream of acid flowing downwards over inert stone packing. This acid consists of a mixture of weak chamber acid (66% H_2SO_4) and acid from the Gay-Lussac tower (78% H_2SO_4 in which have been absorbed the nitrogen oxides emerging from the lead chambers, probably combined as nitrosyl-sulphuric acid, $NO.HSO_4$).

The mixed acids are delivered to the top of the Glover tower and flow down over the packing. Nitrogen oxides are liberated from the Gay-Lussac acid:

$$H_2O + 2NO.HSO_4 \rightarrow 2H_2SO_4 + NO_2 + NO$$

The hot burner gases pick up the oxides of nitrogen and carry them into the lead chambers. During their passage through the Glover tower the gases cool from about 600° C. to about 90° C., the heat lost having been used to concentrate the weak chamber acid flowing down the tower. The Glover acid flowing from the base of the tower is about 78% H_2SO_4.

One form of packing inside a modern Glover tower consists of acid-resisting bricks arranged in chequer fashion so that there are spaces between them. The walls are of lead, lined with brick.

Apart from bringing about the liberation of nitrogen oxides, the Glover tower serves to concentrate the chamber acid and to cool the hot burner gases to a temperature suitable for the lead chamber reaction.

The oxidation of sulphur dioxide and production of sulphuric acid begin inside the Glover tower.

Inevitably there is a small wastage of nitrogen oxides during the Chamber Process, some of which is caused by reduction below nitric oxide. This is normally made good in modern plant by introducing additional supplies of nitric oxide between the Glover tower and the lead chambers. This is produced by the catalytic oxidation of ammonia, which is passed, mixed with air, through a woven gauze of platinum wire at 900° C. approximately:

$$4NH_3 + 5O_2 \rightarrow 4NO + 6H_2O$$

The Lead Chambers

When they leave the Glover tower the gases consist of sulphur dioxide, steam, oxygen, oxides of nitrogen and inert gases from the air. The gases are at a temperature of about 90° C.

Inside the lead chambers the sulphur dioxide is oxidised by atmospheric oxygen in the presence of water, which enters through the roof of the chamber as a fine spray:

$$2H_2O + 2SO_2 + O_2 \rightarrow 2H_2SO_4$$

This reaction will take place slowly in the absence of oxides of nitrogen, but is accelerated when they are present. They act as oxygen carriers by a reduction/oxidation reaction between NO_2 and NO, which can be expressed generally as*

$$H_2O + SO_2 + NO_2 \rightarrow H_2SO_4 + NO$$
$$2NO + O_2 \rightarrow 2NO_2$$

The nitrogen peroxide thus provides oxygen for the SO_2, the nitric oxide formed being reconverted to nitrogen peroxide by the oxygen in the chamber (suggested by Péligot in 1844).

Berzelius in 1830, and Weber in 1866, suggested that nitrogen trioxide was the active agent:

$$H_2O + SO_2 + N_2O_3 \rightarrow H_2SO_4 + 2NO$$
$$4NO + O_2 \rightarrow 2N_2O_3$$

Water is now sprayed into the chambers directly instead of being brought in as steam. Oxidation of sulphur dioxide is an exothermic reaction. 1 kg. of H_2SO_4 produced liberates 600–700 calories when water is used, as against 800–900 calories in the case of steam. By keeping the reaction temperature low (below 90° C.), corrosion of the lead is kept at a minimum and the acid condenses more easily. The last chamber is usually kept as low as 20–30° C., and the gases are sometimes passed through a cooler before entering the Gay-Lussac tower. The oxides of nitrogen are absorbed more efficiently at lower temperatures.

---

* See Chemistry of Process, p. 24.

The concentration of acid produced in the lead chambers is regulated carefully. Too strong an acid will dissolve oxides of nitrogen to form nitrosylsulphuric acid, which will attack the lead. Weak acid is equally undesirable, as it causes the oxides of nitrogen to dissolve as nitric acid, which collects in the chamber acid.

Much of the water needed during the lead chamber reaction is provided by evaporation from the weak acid flowing down the Glover tower. The additional water supplied by the spray must be regulated with great care.

The acid which condenses in the lead chambers is drawn off as Chamber Acid, at a concentration of 50–70%. Much of it returns to the Glover tower, where it is concentrated to Glover Acid of about 78%.

The sulphuric acid plant normally contains a number of chambers, the gases flowing through from one into the other. The residual gases emerging from the final chamber contain very little sulphur dioxide. About half of the atmospheric oxygen has been used up, and the gases entering the Gay-Lussac tower are essentially oxygen, oxides of nitrogen, nitrogen, and inert gases.

One of the main technical problems is to complete the oxidation of sulphur dioxide in the chambers. As the reaction proceeds, sulphur dioxide is used up and the reaction rate falls. The concentration of oxides of nitrogen must be maintained at a level high enough to ensure that the sulphur dioxide in the last chamber is converted to acid; too high a concentration of oxides of nitrogen has to be avoided. Too intense an activity rapidly corrodes the lead.

The lead chambers are constructed from sheet lead about ⅛ in. thick. In the early sulphuric acid plants they were normally cubical. Many modifications have been made in order to try to increase the speed of the reaction and so raise the output per unit volume from the lead chambers.

An important British development in design, introduced by W. G. Mills and C. T. Packard in 1914, was a plant with chambers constructed in the form of truncated cones, water-cooled on the outside. Mills-Packard chambers occupy less space (and involve less capital cost) than the earlier rectangular ones. Many are now in use in Britain, the Dominions, Europe and the U.S.A.

The *Falding system* employs unusually high chambers. The gases which have reacted and cooled sink to the bottom of the chamber and can be removed to the next one.

The Gay-Lussac Tower

The main constituents of the gases leaving the lead chambers are nitrogen and oxides of nitrogen.

As they enter the base of the Gay-Lussac tower the gases meet a stream of cold concentrated sulphuric acid (78% derived from the Glover tower) which is trickling down inert packing from a tank at the top of the tower. The oxides of nitrogen are absorbed by combining to form nitrosyl-sulphuric acid

$$4NO + O_2 + 4H_2SO_4 \rightarrow 4NO.HSO_4 + 2H_2O$$

The Gay-Lussac acid, after leaving the tower, is pumped to the top of the Glover tower.

Modern Gay-Lussac towers are taller and narrower than Glover towers and are packed with acid-proof rings. There are usually two towers in series. After passing through the Gay-Lussac tower the residual gas consists mainly of atmospheric nitrogen which has passed through the process unchanged, together with the essential excess oxygen at about 5%.

Tower Systems

Many attempts have been made to dispense with the lead chambers by using packed towers in which the reaction takes place more rapidly. The first step in this development was the use of towers between the chambers. Experiments with inter-chamber towers were carried out by Lunge during the early years of the present century.

In 1905 Hugo Petersen introduced a tower between the last chamber of the sulphuric acid plant and the Gay-Lussac tower. This tower was fed with low density nitrous vitriol which was recirculated through the tower. If any excess sulphur dioxide remained in the gases leaving the last chamber it was oxidised in the tower, nitrogen oxides being given up by the acid. If there was no sulphur dioxide present the acid would take up nitrogen oxides, thus making up any previous loss sustained during oxidation of excess sulphur dioxide.

Petersen developed his invention into a system in which the chambers were replaced entirely by packed towers. Such plants have been built in many countries, and their use is still extending. Orthodox raw materials are used, and in addition the system is useful for dilute and fluctuating sulphur dioxide feeds such as those obtained from waste metallurgical gases.

21

A typical Petersen plant consists of five towers constructed of acid-resisting masonry. The first tower is a denitrating tower, the second and third are production towers, and the remaining two towers are Gay-Lussacs.

The denitrating tower works in a similar way to a Glover tower. Acid from it is fed to the final Gay-Lussac tower and then flows through the towers in reverse order to that followed by the gas.

NOTE. *The over-all yield of sulphuric acid from the Chamber Process is about 95–98% of theory.*

The Chamber Process is an economical way of making dilute sulphuric acid when it is not required in an extremely pure state. The purity of the incoming sulphur dioxide is not a critical factor, and any raw material providing sulphur dioxide can be used. The acid may contain a fairly high proportion of impurities, depending on the nature of the raw material used.

CHEMISTRY OF THE CHAMBER PROCESS

Although it is generally accepted that nitrogen dioxide provides oxygen for the oxidation of sulphur dioxide, and the resulting nitric oxide is then reoxidised by air, this only gives a general idea of what happens inside the lead chamber. The modern theory of the reactions therein is very much more involved.

G. Lunge in 1885 [1] and 1888 [2] suggested that inside the Glover tower the sulphur dioxide reacts with nitric acid:

$$HNO_3 + SO_2 \rightarrow NO.HSO_4$$
$$\text{Nitrosylsulphuric acid}$$

The nitrosylsulphuric acid then reacts with further quantities of sulphur dioxide and water:

$$2H_2O + SO_2 + 2NO.HSO_4 \rightarrow 3H_2SO_4 + 2NO$$

Nitric oxide reacts readily with oxygen, forming nitrogen dioxide. Inside the chambers these two gases are both present, with nitric oxide in excess in the early stages and in equimolecular proportion later (i.e. N_2O_3).

With water the N_2O_3 yields nitrous acid:

$$H_2O + N_2O_3 \rightarrow 2HNO_2$$

The nitrous acid then reacts with sulphur dioxide and oxygen to form nitrosylsulphuric acid:

$$2HNO_2 + 2SO_2 + O_2 \rightarrow 2NO.HSO_4$$

22

Sulphur storage vats at Texas sulphur well

Liquid sulphur from wells being distributed in storage vats, where it hardens as it cools

Anhydrite mine, 800 ft. below the works of I.C.I., Billingham Division, in Co. Durham

Anhydrite kiln in the sulphuric acid plant of I.C.I., Billingham Division

In the presence of water this breaks down into sulphuric acid and nitrous acid:

$$NO.HSO_4 + H_2O \rightarrow H_2SO_4 + HNO_2$$

A further investigation of the process was later carried out by Lunge and E. Berl, who published their theory in 1906 [3]. It introduced a modification into the earlier one by recognising the transient formation of sulphonitronic acid (SO_5NH_2) in the chambers. This acid was an intermediate product in the formation of nitrosylsulphuric acid.

The theory was confirmed by later researches of Berl [4], and the mechanism now accepted is as follows:

(1) $2NO + O_2 \rightarrow 2NO_2$

(2) $H_2O + SO_2 \rightarrow H_2SO_3$

(3) $H_2SO_3 + NO_2 \rightarrow SO_5NH_2$

(4) $2SO_5NH_2 + NO_2 \rightarrow 2NO.HSO_4 + H_2O + NO$

(5) $2NO.HSO_4 + SO_2 + 2H_2O \rightleftharpoons 2SO_5NH_2 + H_2SO_4$

(4a) $SO_5NH_2 \rightleftharpoons H_2SO_4 + NO$

(5a) $4NO.HSO_4 + 2H_2O \rightleftharpoons 4H_2SO_4 + 4NO + O_2$

(5b) $NO.HSO_4 + HNO_3 \rightleftharpoons H_2SO_4 + 2NO_2$

(b) Contact Process

The Contact Process for manufacturing sulphuric acid is based on the oxidation of sulphur dioxide to sulphur trioxide in the presence of solid catalysts such as vanadium pentoxide or platinum. It dates from 1831, when Peregrine Phillips, a British vinegar manufacturer, discovered that sulphur dioxide and air drawn through a heated tube containing finely divided platinum were largely converted into sulphur trioxide.

In his patent Phillips suggested absorbing the sulphur trioxide in water. The modern method uses sulphuric acid instead of water; apart from this, the present-day Contact Process is basically the same as that described by Phillips more than a century ago.

The Contact Process was slow to develop on a commercial scale because the mechanisms of the reactions involved were not properly understood. It was not until 1901 that the underlying principles were clearly defined by Knietsch in a paper to the German Chemical Society.

The pioneer plant in Britain was erected by W. S. Squire and R. Messel at Silvertown, London, in 1875. By 1914 three Contact plants were in operation in Britain.

Development of the Contact Process was speeded up by the demand for fuming sulphuric acid (oleum), needed for the rapidly growing dyestuffs industry. Fuming sulphuric acid cannot be made by the Chamber Process.

The Badische Contact Process, started in Germany in 1901, was the first to make use of Knietsch's fundamental researches. It showed that under production conditions an excess of oxygen in the air/sulphur dioxide mixture (from the burners) was needed, and that the converter (in which these gases pass over platinum catalyst) must be cooled and not heated. The harmful effect of impurities on the platinum catalyst (first noticed by Squire and Messel in 1895) was also examined in detail and the necessity for careful gas purification made clear.

In modern Contact plants the principles have remained unchanged, but attempts have been made to find catalysts other than platinum, which is expensive, comparatively scarce and susceptible to poisoning by impurities. Many alternative catalysts have been examined, but only ferric oxide and vanadium pentoxide have been of industrial value. Ferric oxide is of limited efficiency, and vanadium pentoxide has proved to be the main competitor of platinum.

The advantages claimed for vanadium pentoxide include greater freedom from poisoning effects and lower initial cost. The used catalyst has, however, no salvage value.

The catalyst is carried on perforated shelves inside a cylindrical iron or steel vessel called a converter. The sulphur dioxide is normally oxidised in stages by passing the gases through a series of converters.

Before entering the first converter the mixture of sulphur dioxide and air is heated in a heat exchange unit to 400–450° C., the optimum working temperature for the catalyst. The gas enters the top of the first converter and passes downwards through one or more layers of catalyst consisting of an inert carrier, such as silica gel, impregnated with finely divided vanadium pentoxide or platinum, thus exposing the maximum surface area of catalyst to the reaction mixture. Part of the sulphur dioxide is oxidised to sulphur trioxide:

$$2SO_2 + O_2 \rightleftharpoons 2SO_3$$

The reaction is exothermic, and the gas leaves the converter at about 580° C. The temperature of the gas and the catalyst is not allowed to exceed 600° C., for this temperature favours the dissociation of the sulphur trioxide and above it the catalyst tends to deteriorate.

Before entering a second converter the gas passes through a heat exchange unit. Here it gives up its excess heat to incoming sulphur dioxide gas, the temperature of which is raised to the 400–450° C. level at which it enters the first converter.

The partly converted gas then passes into the second converter, having been cooled to 400–450° C.

In the modern Contact plant the gas may pass through two, three or four conversion stages. Between each converter it is cooled by means of a heat exchange unit, so that the temperature of the gas leaving the final converter does not exceed 480° C.

At that stage 95–98% of the sulphur dioxide has been converted to sulphur trioxide.

After leaving the converter unit the gases are cooled and then enter the absorber tower, where sulphuric acid is formed by combination of sulphur trioxide and water. It would be impracticable at this stage to use water for absorption, but sulphur trioxide dissolves easily in strong sulphuric acid. The gas enters the base of the absorbing tower and meets a stream of sulphuric acid descending over the packing in the tower. The sulphur trioxide combines with the water in the acid, which leaves the tower as 99% H_2SO_4 approximately.

Water is added to the acid as it leaves the tower to maintain a constant strength. The heat evolved when the sulphur trioxide dissolves in the sulphuric acid, and when the acid is later diluted with water, results in a rise in temperature. The acid is cooled by passing it through banks of water-cooled pipes, and is then pumped to the top of the absorber tower and recirculated.

The residual gas, containing nitrogen, oxygen, and a very small amount of unconverted sulphur dioxide, escapes to the atmosphere. The trace of unconverted sulphur dioxide is sometimes converted to sulphite by absorption in solutions of alkalis.

CHEMISTRY OF THE CONTACT PROCESS

The catalytic oxidation of sulphur dioxide to sulphur trioxide in the Contact Process is a gas reaction at the surface of a solid catalyst. This is one of the most important classes of industrial catalytic reactions, including, for example, the production of ammonia, the oxidation of ammonia to nitric acid, and numerous hydrogenation reactions. The reaction is reversible:

$$2SO_2 + O_2 \rightleftharpoons 2SO_3$$

25

This equilibrium, studied according to the Law of Mass Action, gives the following relationships:

$$K = \frac{[SO_3]^2}{[O_2][SO_2]^2}$$

$$\text{or} \quad K[O_2][SO_2]^2 = [SO_3]^2$$

$$\text{or} \quad K[O_2] = \frac{[SO_3]^2}{[SO_2]^2}$$

Formation of sulphur trioxide is therefore increased by raising the concentration of either oxygen or sulphur dioxide. In practice, the object is to increase the conversion of sulphur dioxide rather than that of oxygen; an excess of oxygen is therefore provided.

An excessive concentration of oxygen gives high conversion but a low intake of sulphur dioxide; as a result, the production rate of sulphur trioxide is low. Oxygen concentration is therefore limited to a slight excess, and a high intake of sulphur dioxide is maintained. In this way *optimum* conversion as distinct from *maximum* conversion is obtained.

The reaction is exothermic, and care has to be taken to control the temperature of the converter:

$$SO_2 + \tfrac{1}{2}O_2 \rightarrow SO_3 + 22,600 \text{ cal.}$$

Rise in temperature increases the rate at which equilibrium is reached and decreases the equilibrium concentration of sulphur trioxide.

With vanadium pentoxide catalysts the optimum conversion temperatures at various points in the converter system fall within the range 450–580° C. Special types of platinised asbestos catalysts will operate efficiently at initial temperatures below 400° C.

At these temperatures conversion is rapid and the equilibrium conditions are such as to favour high concentrations of sulphur trioxide. The reaction velocity is high enough to permit a rapid passage of gas through the converter.

Iron oxide does not function well as a catalyst until the temperature is about 600° C. This high temperature, by shifting the equilibrium towards the left, reduces the concentrations obtainable and makes the output poorer.

STATISTICS OF MANUFACTURE

In 1950 the world production of sulphuric acid in countries outside the Iron Curtain was more than 23,500,000 tons a year. Over 1,800,000 tons were manufactured in the United Kingdom.

In the United Kingdom the amounts of acid made from the various raw materials were as follows:

	Tons of Acid	Per cent. of Total
Sulphur and H₂S	1,032,000	57·4
Pyrites	266,500	14·8
Spent oxide	254,500	14·1
Smelter gases	146,000	8·1
Anhydrite	101,000	5·6

20·7% of British sulphuric acid production was from indigenous raw materials. Of these, anhydrite is the only one available in unlimited supply.

Approximately 1,120,000 tons of British sulphuric acid production in 1950 was by the Contact Process and 680,000 tons by the Chamber Process.

In 1953, 1,875,000 tons of sulphuric acid were made in the United Kingdom, 1,217,000 tons by the Contact Process and 658,000 tons by the Chamber Process.

B

TECHNICAL DATA

Formula H_2SO_4

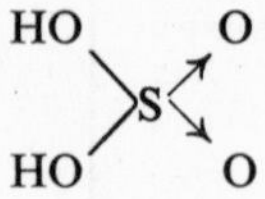

$$\begin{array}{c} HO \\ \\ HO \end{array} \!\!\! S \!\!\! \begin{array}{c} O \\ \\ O \end{array}$$

General Properties

Concentrated sulphuric acid (or oil of vitriol) is a water-white, heavy, viscous liquid. It is highly corrosive and has a great affinity for water, with which it can react with explosive violence.

It removes the elements of water from most forms of organic matter, such as wood, sugar, oxalic acid, formic acid, etc.

Sulphuric acid is a strong dibasic acid which forms salts with metals or their oxides, carbonates, etc., e.g.:

$NaHSO_4$ (sodium hydrogen sulphate) Na_2SO_4 (sodium sulphate)
$Al_2(SO_4)_3$ (aluminium sulphate) $ZnSO_4$ (zinc sulphate)
$(NH_4)_2SO_4$ (ammonium sulphate) $CuSO_4$ (copper sulphate)

The concentrated acid is useful as a dehydrating agent because of its strong affinity for water.

Physical Constants of 100% H_2SO_4

Specific gravity at 15·5° C.: 1·8391.
Boiling point: About 338° C. (Above the boiling point the vapour begins to dissociate into sulphur trioxide (SO_3) and water, being completely dissociated at 450° C.)
Freezing point: 10° C.

Grades

The principal grades of sulphuric acid are:
Concentrated sulphuric acid (concentrated oil of vitriol, C.O.V.; rectified oil of vitriol, R.O.V.): 93–98% H_2SO_4.
Brown oil of vitriol (B.O.V.) 77–78% H_2SO_4.
Battery or accumulator acid: Generally supplied as 98% H_2SO_4 or dilute acid (28–33% H_2SO_4).
Reagent quality and B.P. acid: 98% H_2SO_4.

28

Sulphur trioxide monohydrate: 100% H_2SO_4.

Oleum (fuming sulphuric acid): Oleum is formed by dissolving SO_3 in 100% H_2SO_4 to produce $H_2S_2O_7$. Thus 20% oleum is 20 parts SO_3 + 80 parts 100% H_2SO_4.

Handling and Transport

Sulphuric acid attacks most metals. The degree of attack on iron and steel is greater with dilute than with strong acid, the converse being true for lead. Thus, R.O.V. and B.O.V. may be handled, stored or transported in mild steel, but lower-strength acid must be used in lead or suitable lined containers. Pure acid (Reagent or B.P. qualities) is stored in glass-lined vessels.

Road or rail tank wagons: B.O.V., R.O.V., 20% oleum.

Drums: All strengths over 93%, including 65% oleum.

Winchesters and carboys: Small quantities of all strengths with the exception of oleum.

C

INDUSTRIAL USES OF SULPHURIC ACID

Superphosphate

In 1840 Liebig published his classic theory of the nutrition of plants and showed the feasibility of supplying calcium and phosphates to growing plants in the form of ground bones. Liebig also showed that the addition of sulphuric acid to the bones gave a phosphate more quickly available to the plants.

In Britain John Bennet Lawes began field trials at Rothamsted in 1834, and in 1842 he patented a process for producing the so-called "superphosphate" (containing the more soluble calcium dihydrogen phosphate) by the action of sulphuric acid on mineral calcium phosphate:

$$Ca_3(PO_4)_2 + 2H_2SO_4 \rightarrow Ca(H_2PO_4)_2 + 2CaSO_4$$

Lawes was the world pioneer of the industry, and in 1854 Packard erected a complete superphosphate factory (including the manufacture of sulphuric acid) at Ipswich.

Today superphosphate manufacture is the biggest single user of sulphuric acid.

Sulphate of Ammonia

Ammonium sulphate, like superphosphate, is another extremely important chemical fertilizer. For many years it has been manufactured by absorbing by-product ammonia, obtained from gasworks and coke ovens, in sulphuric acid. Although large quantities of sulphate of ammonia are now made from synthetic ammonia and calcium sulphate (anhydrite):

$$2NH_3 + H_2O + CaSO_4 + CO_2 \rightarrow (NH_4)_2SO_4 + CaCO_3$$

the by-product method still makes the second-largest demand on sulphuric acid in Britain.

Manufacture of Rayon and Transparent Paper

Large quantities of sulphuric acid are used during the viscose process for making rayon (artificial silk). The acid is used in the spinning bath, where the viscose solution reverts to cellulose. The viscose may be used as either yarn or fibres, or in the form of transparent paper for wrapping food, etc.

Glover tower

Burner house

Lead chambers

First Gay-Lussac tower

Final Gay-Lussac tower

Exit gas

A typical lead-chamber plant

In some modern plants, like that shown, the circular-section Mills Packard water-cooled lead chambers have replaced the old square type

(a)   (b)

Contact plant. Converter unit, showing from left to right:
(a) *heat interchanger*
(b) *converter consisting of four separate catalyst vessels superimposed*

Pickling of Metals

This is an application of far-reaching importance, since pickling is employed at some stage or other in the fabrication of an almost limitless variety of articles produced from iron and steel. Pickling is, in effect, treatment with acid to remove the oxide film from steel sheet, wire and fabricated articles before such finishing processes as galvanising, tinning, plating or enamelling; unless this film is removed subsequent coatings do not adhere to the metal.

Pigments for Paints

Sulphuric acid is used in the preparation of many pigments, including "blanc fixe" (barium sulphate), lithopone (zinc sulphide and barium sulphate) and the increasingly important titanium dioxide pigments. These are valuable in that (unlike white lead) they are not blackened by hydrogen sulphide, which is often present in the air of towns.

Explosives

The nitrating acid used in the preparation of nitroglycerine, guncotton, T.N.T., picric acid, etc., is a mixture of concentrated nitric and concentrated sulphuric acids. Large amounts of sulphuric acid are thus used to prepare the explosives needed for the winning of coal and minerals from mines and quarries, as well as for military applications.

Refining of Petroleum Oils

The use of sulphuric acid to remove sulphur derivatives and unsaturated compounds from petroleum oils is likely to increase in this country with the large expansion of the oil-refining industry now in progress.

Dyestuffs

Since the middle of the nineteenth century sulphuric acid has been used in the making of intermediates and dyestuffs, and many thousands of tons of acid are now used each year in Britain for this purpose.

Hydrochloric Acid and Saltcake

Although a purer-quality hydrochloric acid is now produced by combining hydrogen and chlorine, large quantities are still produced by treating salt with sulphuric acid:

$$2NaCl + H_2SO_4 \rightarrow Na_2SO_4 + 2HCl$$

The by-product sodium sulphate ("saltcake") is important in the glass and papermaking industries and for making sodium sulphide (used in the tanning trade).

Accumulators

The acid is used not only as the electrolyte in accumulators but also in the manufacture of their plates.

Other Uses

Only the larger consumers have been mentioned above, but thousands of tons of acid are used every year for innumerable other purposes—as a weedkiller, for making plastics, in the textile and leather trades, and for making all manner of other chemicals such as the sulphates of copper, magnesium, aluminium and zinc, dichromates and chromic acid, borax, formic acid and tartaric acid.

Statistics of Uses

In 1953 the amount of sulphuric acid (per cent. of total) used by various industries in Britain was as follows:

	%
Superphosphate	25·4
Sulphate of ammonia	15·1
Rayon and transparent paper ..	12·2
Titanium oxide	8·9
Iron and steel pickling	5·1
Dyestuffs	3·6
Oil refining	3·4
Hydrochloric acid	2·9
Explosives	1·7
Soap and Glycerine	1·6

D

SULPHURIC ACID PRODUCTION IN BRITAIN

The development of the Frasch process has made America the world's largest sulphur producer. The sulphur domes in Texas and Louisiana supply some 90% of the total world output. The product is extremely pure and eminently suitable for burning to sulphur dioxide, which requires little further purification for use in the Contact Process.

In 1926, when 722,000 tons of sulphuric acid were made in Britain, less than 70,000 tons of sulphur were used. That is to say, three-quarters of the output was from other raw materials. In 1950, on the other hand, nearly 60% of the total production of 1,800,000 tons was made by burning 360,000 tons of sulphur. Not only had the overall output of acid doubled in 24 years, but the dependence on sulphur as the raw material had more than doubled as well.

In comparison with other raw materials, sulphur requires cheaper and simpler plant which is easier and cleaner to operate. Sulphur needs less shipping space than pyrites, so that during the second world war an additional impetus was given to its use. By 1950 Britain was importing sulphur from America at the rate of nearly half a million tons a year for acid manufacture and other purposes.

During that year, however, the American sulphur situation became critical. Post-war demands were rising steeply, particularly in the U.S., and the stores of sulphur in America fell to a dangerous level. Production could not keep pace with demand. Moreover, the sulphur domes were not inexhaustible. At these new very high levels of demand it appeared that proved reserves which had formerly seemed adequate for many years might be sufficient only for a decade or two. As a result the United States Government was obliged to take drastic action by rationing available supplies of sulphur to its consumers.

In 1951 British sulphur requirements were estimated at approximately 400,000 tons for sulphuric acid and 100,000 tons for other products. During the first quarter Britain was allocated 82,000 tons—about two-thirds of the quarterly requirement. A further 19,000 tons were released later. As a result, acid production had to be reduced. This was the cause of the "sulphur crisis" which affected Britain during 1950–1 even more seriously than the shortage of coal.

As sulphuric acid is such a widely used industrial raw material, curtailment of its production was felt throughout most industries in the country.

Meanwhile every attempt was made to develop new sources of raw materials for sulphuric acid—not only as a short-term measure, but in planning for the future against the eventual exhaustion of American sulphur deposits.

The Sicilian industry received a new lease of life. Arrangements were also made to develop volcanic deposits in Japan and South America. Plans were made in Britain to make the fullest use of other raw materials. Spent oxide burning was increased to capacity, and a small contribution of sulphur was made by the British oil refineries. Sulphur-burning plants were converted to enable them to use pyrites.

Of all the established raw materials, only anhydrite was available in unlimited supply in Britain. Production of sulphur dioxide and sulphuric acid from anhydrite has been carried out at Billingham, Co. Durham, since 1930. The plant, however, is complicated; its capital cost is much higher than that of a pyrites plant producing sulphuric acid only and is slightly higher than the cost of a sulphuric acid plant based on pyrites together with a conventional cement plant working on calcium carbonate. Comparison of production costs for the different processes depends, of course, on the relative prices of anhydrite, sulphur and pyrites as raw materials and the realisation on by-products. Figures have, however, been published to show that with sulphur and pyrites at 1952 prices and assuming that anhydrite is available in Great Britain near the plants that will use it, the net cost of sulphuric acid made from anhydrite, after allowing for the realisation on sale of cement, can be lower than that produced from sulphur or pyrites, although the capital investment is higher. During 1951, plans were made to increase production of sulphuric acid from anhydrite in Britain. It is probable that this process will play an increasing part in future production of sulphuric acid; it will help to solve the problem set by a possible diminution in American sulphur supplies.

In other countries similar plants have been constructed to produce acid either from anhydrite or from gypsum. In Germany the anhydrite plant which began operating at Wolfen in 1938 was planned to increase output to 175,000 tons of acid a year by 1955. A French plant using gypsum started producing acid in 1937 and is rated at 25,000 tons a year. In Poland an anhydrite plant of unknown capacity was being built in 1951.

34

In Britain the Billingham plant, which came into production in 1930, planned to increase output to 175,000 tons a year, and a plant on Merseyside to be completed after 1954 has a planned output of 150,000 tons a year. A plant is planned for erection in Cumberland with an output of 70,000 tons a year.

As a result of the sulphur crisis a number of other sources of sulphur were considered on a long-term basis.

The microbiological reduction of inorganic sulphates is a common process in nature. Hydrogen sulphide is produced; when this is oxidised in the presence of iron salts free sulphur is formed. In certain lakes in North Africa sulphur has been produced in large amounts in this way. The process has been considered with a view to its use on a commercial scale, but this is essentially a long-term project.

In the crude oil which is brought into Britain for refining there is an average of about 2% of sulphur. With British refineries handling some 20 million tons of oil a year, this is equivalent to about 400,000 tons of sulphur. Extraction is, however, a difficult problem.

Recovery of sulphur from coke-oven gas could make almost 100,000 tons of sulphur available annually in Britain, and the coal burned in British power stations every year contains up to 400,000 tons of sulphur.

CONCLUSION

The development of sources of sulphur for sulphuric acid production is one of the most challenging technical problems of modern times. The consumption of sulphuric acid increased steadily after the end of World War II, corresponding to the increasing tempo of modern industry.

In 1938 production in Britain was 995,000 tons; in 1944 it was 1,268,000 tons and in 1953, 1,875,000 tons.

A prolonged curtailment of sulphuric acid supplies could cripple British industrial economy more seriously than a shortage of any other raw material, even including coal.

REFERENCES
[1] *J. Chem. Soc.*, **47**, 470 (1885).
[2] *Ber.* **21**, 67 and 3323 (1888).
[3] *Z. Angew. Chem.*, **19**, 807, 857 and 881 (1906).
[4] *Trans. Am. Inst. Chem. Eng.*, **31**, 193 (1935).

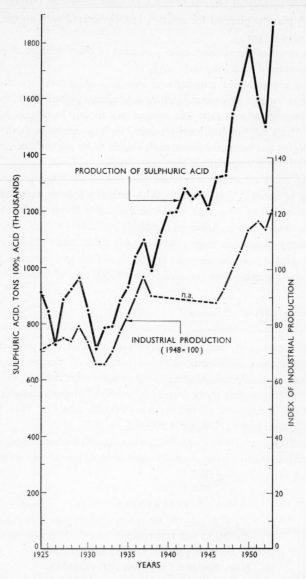

*Comparison of sulphuric acid production with
industrial production in the United Kingdom*

BIBLIOGRAPHY

MANNING J., FERTILIZER SOCIETY. "Sulphuric Acid and Cement from Anhydrite" (Paper read before the Fertilizer Society in London on 8th November 1951). Pp. 30. (London, Fertilizer Society.)

LUNGE, G., *et al.* *Manufacture of Acids and Alkalis.* (London, Gurney and Jackson, 1925.)
 Vol. 1. Raw Materials for the Manufacture of Sulphuric Acid.
 Vol. 2. Manufacture of Sulphuric Acid (Chamber Process).
 Vol. 3. The Concentration of Sulphuric Acid.
 Vol. 4. Manufacture of Sulphuric Acid (Contact Process).

BEDWELL, W. L., ROYAL INSTITUTE OF CHEMISTRY. Lectures, Monographs and Reports, 1952, No. 3: Production of Sulphuric Acid from Calcium Sulphate, pp. 21. (London, Royal Institute of Chemistry, 1952.)

FAIRLIE, A. M. Sulphuric Acid Manufacture. Pp. 632. (New York, Reinhold, 1936.)

NOTES